DISCOVER THE MAGIC OF RAINBOWS

Text © 2010 Dick Evans
Illustrations © 2010 Dick Evans

All rights reserved. No part of this publication may be reproduced or transmitted in any form without written permission from the publisher. Exceptions are made for brief excerpts used in published reviews.

Bear Clause Publications
www.BearClausePublications.com

Evans, Dick.
   Discover the magic of rainbows : Annie Oxidant finds the path to healthy foods / written and illustrated by Dick Evans. — Traverse City, Mich. : Bear Clause Publications, c2010.

      p. ; cm.

      ISBN: 978-0-9798363-3-6
      Audience: Young children.
      Summary: While looking for treasure at the end of the rainbow, Annie Oxidant and her dog meet farmer Brock O'Lee; who shows them how to find healthy foods by using the colors in the rainbow.

      1. Food habits—Juvenile literature. 2. Vegetables in human nutrition—Juvenile literature. 3. Fruit in human nutrition—Juvenile literature. 4. Children—Nutrition—Requirements—Juvenile literature. 5. Food habits. 6. Vegetables. 7. Fruit. 8. Nutrition. I. Title.

QP141 .E93 2010   2010908785

613.2—dc22   1008

Printed in Canada
10 9 8 7 6 5 4 3 2 1

Interior layout by www.tothepointsolutions.com

For large order discounts contact the publisher.

DISCOVER THE **MAGIC** OF RAINBOWS

Annie Oxidant Finds the Path to Healthy Foods

Written and illustrated by DICK EVANS

BEAR CLAUSE PUBLICATIONS

Annie Oxidant reads a book about rainbows to her dog, Phyto.

Annie and Phyto love rainbows because

at the end of each rainbow is a hidden treasure.

Annie and Phyto decide to find the end of the rainbow.

Along the way, they meet a cow holding a sign. "We are looking for the end of the rainbow," said Annie.

"Oh, you will love the treasure!" said the cow.
"The end is just over that hill."

Annie was so excited she forgot to ask the cow about the sign.

Annie and Phyto were getting closer.
When they reached the end—they found
a stand of fresh fruits and vegetables.

"Where is the *treasure*?" asked Annie.

Phyto was disappointed, too.

"You're looking at it!" said a voice behind them.

They turned and saw Brock O'Lee, a friendly farmer.

"All I see are fruits and vegetables," said Annie.

"That *is* the treasure!" said Farmer Brock. "You can eat a rainbow, you know."

"That's impossible!" said a nearby voice. "You can't eat rainbows. They are in the sky." It was Rudy Baga, Annie's neighbor who thought he knew everything. He seemed pretty sure about this.

"You are partly right," said Farmer Brock. "You can't eat a rainbow in the sky—but when it touches the ground, magic happens. It turns into treasures you *can* eat."

Annie and Rudy wondered what Farmer Brock
meant. Phyto was tired of all the talk about

eating rainbows. He was getting hungry. He decided to dig for real treasure—bones!

Farmer Brock
laughed. He
could tell Annie
and Rudy were
confused.
He needed
to explain
the magic
of rainbows.
"Rainbows have
many colors,"
he said, "like red,
orange, yellow,

green, blue, and purple. The colors occur when sunlight passes through droplets of rain.

"And when sunlight touches the ground it makes colorful things grow."

"See that flower bed over there? Those colors come from sunlight." Farmer Brock paused for a moment and smiled. "And, just like plants, people come in different colors, too."

Rudy wasn't convinced by Farmer Brock's explanation. "Don't you just buy fruits and vegetables at the store? That's where I see them when I go shopping with my mom."

Farmer Brock shook his head. "Let me show you where they really come from. We will follow that rainbow to its beginning."

Farmer Brock led Annie and Rudy down the
path. Phyto wanted to stop and dig for bones.
It seemed like they were wasting a lot of time
talking about rainbows.

"Here is where the rainbow does its magic," said Farmer Brock.

"WOW! Look at all the colors!" said Annie. "It *is* magic! The rainbow is everywhere!"

Farmer Brock explained how the colors in fruits and vegetables worked. "Red fruits and vegetables help you bend and stretch better when you play. They also keep your heart strong and help you remember things. Can you find anything red?"

Rudy picked a tomato. Annie found peppers, lettuce, and radishes. Red vegetables were easy to find!

"What about red fruit?" asked Farmer Brock. Rudy noticed some large watermelon lying in a field next to a strawberry patch.

Annie knew apples and cherries grew on trees. She picked some apples in the orchard.

"There are cranberries in that bog," said Farmer Brock. "Cranberries are really good to eat because they contain a lot of antioxidants—antioxidants keep your body's cells healthy."

"Can you find anything orange?" asked Farmer Brock. "Orange fruit and vegetables help you see better and build strong bones."

"I think Phyto found a carrot," said Annie. "And I see some peppers and squash over there."

Phyto thought the carrot looked like a bone; so he decided to try it. It was tasty and crunchy. He believed orange was good for your eyes. He'd never seen a rabbit wearing glasses ... have you?

"Where are the oranges?" asked Rudy. "Oranges are my favorite fruit."

"Oranges grow where it is warm all year," Farmer Brock explained, "so, you won't find any orange trees here. But, we have peach trees.

"If you can, it is best to eat fresh-picked local fruits and vegetables. That is when they are the best— and it is how farmers make a living. But produce at the grocery store is good for you, too."

Rudy was already looking for yellow fruits and vegetables. He knew he wouldn't find any bananas, pineapples, grapefruits, or lemons because they needed a warm climate, just like oranges.

He found pears and apples in the orchard.

"What do yellow fruits and vegetables do for you?" asked Annie. Her arms were full of squash, beans, and peppers. Phyto loved sweet corn.

"Yellow fruits and vegetables keep you from getting sick," said Farmer Brock. "Wouldn't it be great to not get a cold?"

Farmer Brock was pleased with their next load.
"I see you found the green fruits and vegetables.
They give you lots of energy and help build strong
bones and teeth. Annie, you have parsley, kale,
broccoli, and spinach. Rudy has grapes. Remember,
the darker the color, the better they are for you."

Farmer Brock explained that there were fewer blue and purple fruits and vegetables to choose from. "They help you see better and make your heart stronger. Can you find any?"

Annie picked a bunch of grapes. She saw plums growing in the orchard. Phyto was digging up blue potatoes.

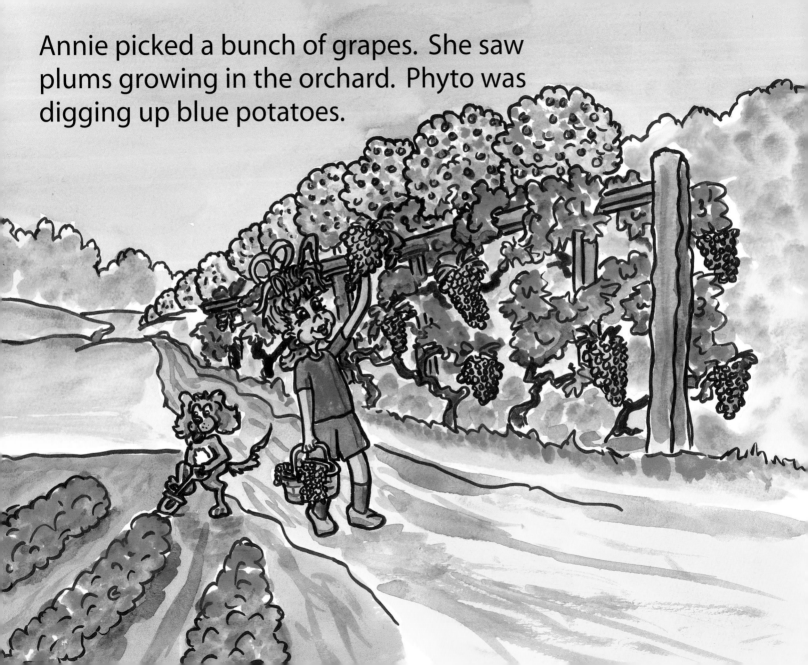

Rudy noticed beets and cabbage. He picked a funny shaped purple vegetable and took it to Farmer Brock. "What is this?" Rudy asked.

"That is an eggplant," said Farmer Brock. "And, no, it won't hatch," he added with a grin. He could tell by Rudy's face what he was thinking.

After they filled the wheelbarrow, Farmer Brock told
Annie and Rudy to pick out their own rainbows. Annie
had a selection of colors in her basket. Rudy only had

red and yellow fruit in his basket. "Rudy," asked
Farmer Brock, "where is your rainbow?"

"I don't have to eat all the colors. I take vitamins."

"Taking vitamins is like eating only one or two colors," Farmer Brock explained. "It is not a rainbow. Fruits and vegetables have everything your body needs to be healthy. They are whole food."

Rudy wanted to be healthy so he chose more colors from the wheelbarrow to add to his basket.

Annie was pleased with her choices. She knew that by eating all the colors of the rainbow, she was going to keep her body strong and healthy.

She could hardly wait to tell her friends about the magic of rainbows.

A NOTE FROM THE AUTHOR

My good friend Nancy Kroupa planted the seed for *Discover the MAGIC of Rainbows* when she said results from an ongoing Juice Plus+ Children's Health Study (childrenshealthstudy.com) identified a lack of educational materials that encourage children to eat a "rainbow diet" of fruits and vegetables. Because of my interest in cartooning and teaching children, she suggested I write a book on the topic.

I hope *Discover the MAGIC of Rainbows* encourages children to look at their plates and ask parents, "Where is the rainbow?" This simple shift in awareness and subsequent change in eating habits could make a major positive difference in the quality of their lives.

As with all books, this project was a group endeavor. I thank everyone who helped, even those I may have forgotten to mention below.

I would like to thank my editor and book designer, Mary Jo Zazueta (tothepointsolutions.com). She makes publishing easy and helps me showcase my work in a quality product. I'd be hard-pressed to do this without her.

I also want to thank Jane Oelke, ND, PhD, who provided valuable nutritional advice; Linda Cole from the Children's Health Study, who helped shape the story line; Cindy Lyskawa and Gayle Gallagher at Copy Queenz, who patiently put up with all the changes I made to the graphics; Sandi McArthur at Oryana Natural Food Co-op, for invaluable advice on teaching the nutrition of whole foods to kids; and to the "Senior Breakfast Club" at Big Boy restaurant in Traverse City, who suffered with great patience during the months of show-and- tell as the book evolved.

And last, but definitely not least, thank you to Jeanette Thompson, a steady, positive influence. Without her encouragement, this book would not have happened.

Author, cartoonist, and art instructor DICK EVANS is also the creator of fun-loving Tourist Country Bear, better known as TC Bear. In *Up North With TC Bear*, his inaugural coloring book, TC Bear travels to Northern Michigan on vacation to enjoy the many year-round activities and attractions that make Up North a special place to visit and live. Children of all ages will enjoy coloring the creative illustrations while remembering their own Up North experiences.

To learn more about this and other books written and illustrated by Dick Evans, and to inquire about drawing classes, please visit:

www.BearClausePublications.com